C000184352

# Contents

Chapter 1

First Warnings. . . . . . . . . . . . . . . . . . . . . . 8

Chapter 2

The Days Before . . . . . . . . . . . . . . . . . . . 20

Chapter 3

The Cyclone Hits. . . . . . . . . . . . . . . . . . . 31

Chapter 4

A Frantic Few Hours . . . . . . . . . . . . . . . 37

Chapter 5

After the Cyclone . . . . . . . . . . . . . . . . . 56

Quiz . . . . . . . . . . . . . . . . . . . . . . . . . . . . . 63

Literacy Skills and Knowledge. . . . . . . . 64

Science Skills and Knowledge. . . . . . . . 66

Glossary. . . . . . . . . . . . . . . . . . . . . . . . . . 68

Quiz Clues . . . . . . . . . . . . . . . . . . . . . . . . 72

Contents

# Cyclones, Hurricanes, and Typhoons

Hurricanes, cyclones, and typhoons all have the same characteristics, but they have different names depending on where they appear:

- hurricanes – North Atlantic Ocean, including Caribbean Sea and Gulf of Mexico
- cyclones – Indian and South Pacific Ocean
- typhoons – North Pacific Ocean, including the Philippines area.

Hurricanes, typhoons, and cyclones are all tropical storms whose winds reach at least 119 kilometres per hour.

They move in a circular direction (clockwise in the southern hemisphere and counter-clockwise in the northern hemisphere) around a relatively calm area known as the *eye*.

The eye is about 30–50 kilometres wide. The most violent activity takes place in the area immediately around the eye, called the *eye wall*.

Tropical storms get their energy from warm tropical seas. The sea's surface temperature must be above 27 degrees Celsius.

# Parts of a Tropical Storm

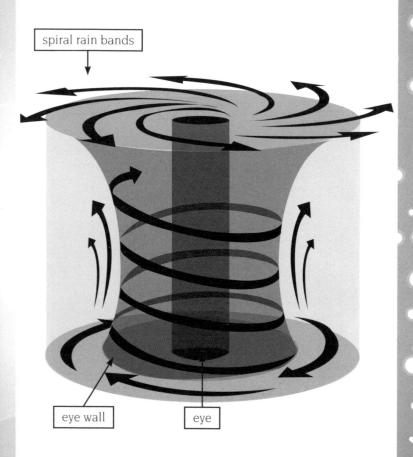

spiral rain bands

eye wall

eye

# Saffir-Simpson Scale

| Category | Speed | Damage |
|---|---|---|
| 1 | 119–153kph | Minimal house damage. Damage to some crops, trees, and caravans. Craft may drag moorings. |
| 2 | 154–177kph | Minor house damage. Significant damage to signs, trees, and caravans. Heavy damage to some crops. Risk of power failure. Small craft may break moorings. |
| 3 | 178–209kph | Some roof and structural damage. Some caravans destroyed. Power failure likely. |
| 4 | 210–249kph | Significant roofing loss and structural damage. Many caravans destroyed and blown away. Dangerous airborne debris. Widespread power failure. |
| 5 | 250+kph | Extremely dangerous with widespread destruction. |

# Tropical Storm Activity Around the World

Arctic Ocean

Pacific Ocean

NORTH AMERICA

Atlantic Ocean

EUROPE

ASIA

Pacific Ocean

AFRICA

Indian Ocean

Equator

Atlantic Ocean

SOUTH AMERICA

AUSTRALIA

Southern Ocean

Australia

Fiji

**Key** ------- tropical storm activity

# *First Warnings*

During January 2003, there were repeated warnings of fierce summer storms north of the Fiji Islands in the South Pacific Ocean. Late on Monday, January 13, the storms had finally developed into Tropical **Cyclone** Ami. After constant monitoring, it became clear that Ami would pass over the island of Vanua Levu, one of the Fijian islands.

### Sunday, 12.00 p.m.

Scruffy bounced around Harley's legs, shaking sand from her black-and-white coat after her sand bath. She always rolled around in the sand after a swim in the lagoon.

A chattering group of Indian myna birds bickered nearby in a tangle of prickly mimosa.

As Harley sauntered along barefoot, he looked at the sky. It was deep blue, just like the sea itself. Scruffy, Harley's dog, loped off along the track towards the house. She stopped and looked back, waiting, tail wagging expectantly.

It was a brilliant day, although there was the threat of a storm later. A light breeze rustled the palm fronds high above Harley's head. They always provided circles of shade from the midday sun. Above the canopy of palms,

Harley could see glimpses of heavy **cumulus clouds** peeping through the ranges to the north. The mountain tops were just visible above the canopy of the tropical rainforest. During this time of year, there were many days when storms developed to the north. It would probably pour later that afternoon. That would bring the temperature down – for a while anyway.

Harley picked up a coconut and bowled it towards Scruffy. It bounced wildly. Scruffy jumped, then bounded after it. She trapped it with her front paws but it was too big to pick up in her mouth.

Harley didn't know what he would do if something happened to his dog. His home was a long way from the nearest village, even further from the small town of Savusavu.

There were no families with kids nearby. In fact, many of the houses along this stretch of dirt road were empty. The people who owned them came in for their holidays, usually after the cyclone season had passed.

Suddenly Harley couldn't see Scruffy. She was up to her usual tricks. Slowly he crept up to the top of the rise, heading for a big, old raintree, whose canopy provided a wide area of open shade near their house. It was a favourite playing and resting space for Scruffy when the skies were clear and the sun was hot. When the **humidity** got too much to do anything else, Harley's mother, Jackie, would sometimes carry out a chair to sit in the leafy cool and read.

In the far side of the raintree's trunk was a large hole, big enough for Harley to slide into if he bent his head. Here, Scruffy often slept in the cool dust or used it as a hiding place when playing games. A family of mongooses had once lived in the hole before Scruffy discovered it.

But today it was too hot even in the shade of the tree. Harley was already sweating as he headed back to the house. Scruffy scampered to her water bowl in the open carport attached to the western side of the building. She lapped noisily.

Inside, Harley drank a glass of cool water that was piped from a spring-fed stream high in the hills behind the property. He continued to sweat. The weather was definitely getting warmer and muggier.

His father, Harry, came out from his office and turned on the short-wave radio. His creased brow showed he had something on his mind.

"That big storm to the north's getting bigger," he said to Harley as he adjusted the radio. Living so far from the main island often made radio reception a problem. Harley wondered why a storm somewhere out in the sea could be so important.

After the news, he heard his father say to his mother, "The storm's building into a severe **depression** and moving south. On its present path, it'll cross the north coast tomorrow."

"But it's still only a big storm," reasoned Jackie, not concerned.

"The conditions seem right," Harry replied.

"But remember conditions can change rapidly," Jackie countered. "**Tropical storms** can be unpredictable and change direction with very little warning."

"So it might go north?" suggested Harley,

"That won't happen, son," replied his father. "In our part of the world, the **southern hemisphere,** tropical storms start during summer near the **Equator** and head south. They usually get bigger as they go. They don't ever go north."

Harley screwed up his nose as his dad continued.

"Now, north of the Equator, it's the opposite. In the **northern hemisphere** the storms head north in the northern summer. But either way, they don't really get going or build up intensity in the first 450 kilometres."

"Are we that close?" asked Harley.

"I wish we were," replied his dad. "It may be safer. We're about 1,500 kilometres south. Plenty of distance for a tropical storm to become a big problem."

Harley rubbed his stomach. He didn't like uncertainty.

"There's no point in worrying, Harley," added his mum. "Once storms hit our island, they usually go east or west around the mountain range and then head off into the South Pacific. There hasn't been a cyclone here for over ten years. Not a bad one in ages."

"There's always a first time," said Harry. "But I'll keep listening to the news. As you say, cyclone movement can be a bit unpredictable."

Early that night, it started to rain heavily. Large drops drummed noisily on the roof and torrents of cool water poured like a waterfall over the guttering right around the house. Lightning flashed and grumpy thunder rumbled and grumbled in the nearby hills.

Scruffy curled up in her kennel at the far end of the carport. She'd never been an inside dog and didn't usually mind storms. The two ginger cats, Macavity and Bella, slept on their cushions on an old park bench near Scruffy's kennel. Their disdain of storms was obvious.

Harley stood silently under the eaves of the veranda and peered south into the night's black heart. There were no other lights. There was nothing between their island and the South Pole.

Harley was very conscious that there were hardly any emergency services, and the ones that they did have were very basic. In fact everything around where they lived was very basic. Electricity had only recently come to the homes and villages along the road from the town. Even the road was basic, just a winding track that followed the beaches and the headland.

Harley was glad that when they had got electricity, his father had kept his generator and solar panels. At least if the cyclone struck, they would still have power. Last time there'd been a storm, the town officials had cut the power at the power station so that no one could get electrocuted by fallen wires.

Harley heard the radio and went inside. They all listened to the news. The storm had intensified, with winds of 70 kilometres per hour. It wasn't officially a cyclone yet, but it had a name, Ami. It was heading south at twelve kilometres an hour.

"Isn't that rather slow for a big storm?" Harley asked, frowning.

"It's going to cover a fair distance in the next 12 hours," his father replied.

"But I thought..." Harley had heard that people in the path of a cyclone could expect winds of more than 160 kilometres an hour. "So how come the winds are 70 kilometres an hour but the storm's moving much more slowly?" he asked, still frowning.

His mum came to the rescue.

"It's like this," she explained. "The cyclone itself is a very big storm. Imagine a giant wheel-like firework cloud. Imagine it's low in the sky. Instead of smoke and sparks that fly out from fireworks, these clouds spit out wind and rain, and sometimes thunderstorms, too.

"If the storm turns into a **hurricane**, it'll work like this," she continued, grabbing a scrap of paper and a pencil and starting to draw.

"These are **spiral bands**," she explained, as she drew spiralling tentacles from the storm's centre. "A cyclone can be 100 kilometres across. It's the whole cyclone that moves slowly, not the winds in it. They could reach 200 kilometres an hour, or more."

"Like a helicopter!" Harley beamed, understanding at last. "The blades go fast but the helicopter can move very slowly."

"And change direction just as quickly!" his dad nodded and grinned.

As Harley's worried look returned, his mother read his mind and said, "Don't worry, Harley. We'll be safe and so will Scruffy and the cats."

Briefly, Harley wondered how wild animals and birds survived cyclones.

## Chapter 2

# *The Days Before*

It rained all that night and continued to bucket down on Monday morning. Harley looked out of his misted bedroom window. He saw that the watercourse that ran past their property, at the bottom of the rise, was swollen and slowly spreading. He looked at the road. The pipes under it were still able to carry the storm water out to the lagoon. Harley tried to guess how long it would be before the road was cut at every low crossing by rising water. The lagoon was no longer a clear azure blue, but a murky grey.

Harley turned his thoughts to Scruffy and went to check on her. She was happily curled up in the back of her kennel. She wagged her tail and it thumped against the kennel's side. Though obviously pleased to see Harley, she made no attempt to leave the safety and comfort of her little home. The cats were curled up asleep on their cushions. It was obvious they had no intention of moving either.

Later that morning, there was a break in the rain. Harley enticed Scruffy out for a quick play. Even on the grass, the water squelched under their feet and mud splashed up their legs. Harley chased Scruffy around some of his dad's smaller hibiscus and fruit trees. He knew that the smaller trees would twist and sway back and forth in the wind and end up making holes that got larger and larger around their trunks. Finally their roots would give up and the trees would be flattened horizontal by the persistent wind.

Back inside, Harley found his parents listening to the storm report. During the night, winds had reached 120 kilometres per hour. Ami had been officially upgraded to a cyclone, Tropical Cyclone Ami, or as they said on the radio, T. C. Ami.

The news report was followed by advice on precautions people should take – things they should do before, and during, the cyclone.

"It may still veer away from us," Jackie reassured Harley.

"The trouble is," said Harry, "even if it gives us a miss, there are so many islands around this region that someone will get a battering."

He stopped talking and listened to the radio again. "All ships in the area have been diverted away from the storm's path. All flights have been cancelled. There'll be no emergency help for many days."

"There won't be much left in the shops in town," added Jackie. "The storm will wipe out the local vegetable gardens. The papaya and mangos will be lost. There'll be no fruit or vegetables for nine to 12 months. There'll probably even be mudslides on some of the cultivated hills. Whole gardens will go."

"I'll go and have a look at the generator, fuel, and batteries," Harry said, pushing open the door and heading for the shed. "I need to be sure everything's working properly."

Just as Harley heard the generator engine roar into life, rain started bucketing down again. Harry had to squelch through the several centimetres of water that were now sitting on the lawn to get back to the house. The branches of the raintrees beyond the back fence drooped down, like old men carrying the weight of the world on their shoulders. Small limbs snapped like brittle icicles under the pressure of the pounding rain and the intensifying **gusts** of wind. The heavy coconut palm fronds hung low, swaying dangerously. In front of the house, the road was flooded, and the murky bay was now dark and angry.

The next afternoon, Harley was once again on the veranda watching the waves crashing on the outer reef then rolling into the beach.

Deep black clouds hovered just above the sea like predators waiting to pounce. They were getting darker, heavier, and more sinister by the moment.

This was Harley's first cyclone, and he didn't know whether to be nervous or excited. He'd seen cyclone damage on TV. He knew people could lose their houses, their animals, and even their lives.

The cyclone warnings were frequent now and advised all people on the island of Vanua Levu to prepare for T. C. Ami.

"Why is it called Ami?" Harley asked his dad as Harry joined him.

"All cyclones have names," Harry replied. "This way, people in different parts of the Pacific don't get the warnings confused. There could be another cyclone off the northern coast of Australia about the same time in the cyclone season. If there was it'd have a different name."

"They're named in alphabetical order using people's names," added his mum, who'd come outside also. "This one's called Ami. The next big storm will be given a name starting with B, the one after that with C, and so on through the alphabet."

"Could be Bert or Bella," laughed Harry. "Later we might have a Macavity. Then a Scruffy! Then next season they'll start the names all over again. But right now we have to deal with Ami, so let's batten down the hatches. You collect up everything in the garden that's not tied down and bring it into the house. Mum'll close the louvres and I'll lock the shutters and put the mesh screens over the glass doors. We don't want tumbling branches and palm fronds whipping them wildly like uncontrollable kites. That could shatter the glass."

"What about Scruffy and the cats?" Harley asked. "Can I bring them inside?"

"There's no need," Harry answered. "They'll be sheltered in the carport. Better they stay there meanwhile."

"But, Dad..." Harley started to protest.

"Not now, Harley," Harry frowned. "Go outside and get everything in, like I told you. If things worsen we'll make another decision about the animals."

Harley stomped off to do as he was told. Then the rains started again.

The next radio report said that T. C. Ami had crossed the north coast and was moving steadily towards where they lived. As it got dark, the winds got stronger and the rain heavier. Although it wasn't cold, Harley shivered and wondered if T. C. Ami would hit that night.

"It's not hurricane-force yet," said Harry.

"I thought it was a cyclone, not a hurricane," said Jackie. "Aren't hurricanes the storms in the Atlantic Ocean?"

"You're right, but the wind speeds also have names. You can get hurricane-force winds in a tropical cyclone. A man called Mr Beaufort came up with names for wind force from calm through to hurricane. They call it the **Beaufort Scale**."

"And where your grandmother grew up in Japan," added Jackie, looking at Harley, "they call cyclones *typhoons*. And in America they are hurricanes." Harley rubbed his stomach again. He was doing it a lot. He said nothing.

### Monday, 9.00 p.m.

Jackie shooed Harley off to bed early while she and Harry listened to the nine o'clock cyclone report. The static on the radio was getting worse and the news was not good, but as yet, even though the winds were stronger and the rain heavier, it seemed no worse than a very severe storm. Maybe, they hoped, Ami would change course and they wouldn't get its full force. It might even be downgraded to a severe tropical storm.

But the wind gusts buffeting the house were getting stronger. Jackie closed the last of the window louvres and checked the others just to be sure.

They went to bed just after the 10 o'clock report. It was more of the same. They weren't sure what else they could do, but they still hoped, against the odds, that T. C. Ami would veer away from them and out into the open Pacific Ocean.

# Chapter 3

# *The Cyclone Hits*

**Tuesday, 12.00 a.m.**

Jackie woke up from a restless sleep. The wind was howling now. The rain was pounding on the roof again and creating the same waterfalls as it had before. Small branches tumbled noisily across the iron roof and disappeared over the other side.

She went into the kitchen and turned on the radio. Through increasing static she heard that there would be danger from low-level land and sea flooding along the coast, and that wind gusts could reach 145 kilometres per hour.

She knew that winds that strong would drive rain under the doors, and between the louvres. It could soon get wet inside!

## Tuesday, 12.30 a.m.

Harry woke up suddenly, alarmed that Jackie was not there. He got up quickly and found her in the kitchen. She repeated what she'd managed to catch on the radio. It wasn't much. They left the radio on, hoping anxiously for updates as they did quick checks of the rooms. Shortly after that, the radio signal was completely drowned out by the static. They were on their own.

Heavier branches began bombarding the

roof and made a frightening racket.

"It's like we're inside a big bass drum," Jackie observed. "I don't know how Harley's managing to sleep through it."

By now, water was oozing under the kitchen door. Harry got the mop and put heavy towels at the base of the kitchen and living room doors, hoping to stop some of the water getting in.

"I'll check the other rooms again," Jackie said. "We need to stop as much water as we possibly can."

When Jackie got to the spare room, she was shocked to see water pouring down the wall from the high louvred air vents. With every wind gust, water sprayed across the room. Not only were the floors flooding, it was raining inside the house!

"Harry!" she yelled. They frantically pulled all the furniture as far from the wall as possible.

"I'll have to go to the shed and get something to fix the air vents," Harry shouted as he rushed out the back door. It was still fairly calm behind the house as he dashed for the shed, just managing to hurdle a large, leafy branch lying on the path. He quickly grabbed a hammer, nails, pieces of wood, and a small stepladder. By the time he got back inside, he was drenched to the skin and needed to change his clothes.

Then the lights went out!

Harry and Jackie's hearts each missed a beat. It was pitch black! But it was only a few moments before the automatic switch on the batteries cut in and the lights came on.

Without comment, Harry and Jackie raced about the house switching off all unnecessary power users. The refrigerator, the deep-freeze unit, the standby on the video player. They had to make the power they had last as long as possible.

## Tuesday, 1.00 a.m.

The din on the roof finally woke Harley. Through the open door, he saw his mother was looking worried. The tiled floor was covered in a thin coat of shimmering water.

He saw his father in one corner yanking on a dry T-shirt. A bundle of wet clothes lay in a heap to one side. He watched as his father hurried into the spare room, closely followed by his mother. Harley got up to see what was going on. He watched his dad place the ladder carefully on the wet floor and quickly test its stability, before scrambling up and urgently nailing small sheets of ply over the air vents.

"We're still going to get flooded, aren't we?" he asked, as the water stopped spraying across the room but still continued to run in ragged rivulets down the wall.

"Help me, Harley!" Jackie shouted, frantically lifting things off the flooded floor and putting them in higher places. Harley grabbed mats, boxes of papers, and shoes and dumped them on the table and in various cupboards.

He could hear palm trees snapping off and falling with frightening thuds on the roof. He shivered – half excited, half scared, not cold.

T. C. Ami was here and she had hit with force!

## Chapter 4

# *A Frantic Few Hours*

**Tuesday, 1.30 a.m.**

As Jackie walked past the phone, she picked up
the receiver. No dial tone! All communication
was now cut. They were completely on their own
with Ami. Then she heard another sound.

"The wind's shifted!" she yelled. "Quick! The
animals! The carport's getting the wind now!"

Forgetting the possible danger, she ran to
the door that led directly to the carport and

opened it. The carport was awash but thankfully the wind on that side of the house was not yet dangerously strong.

"I'm bringing them inside," she yelled over the roar of the wind. She was just in time. The cats and Scruffy were already wide-eyed. If they'd been spooked, they might have made a crazy, fatal dash into the black fury of the storm.

Even inside the house, the cats cowered, fearful of the thumping on the roof and the howling wind.

Scruffy raced over to Harley, who bent down to hug her. She was not going to let him out of her sight again.

"You're going to be just fine now, Scruffy," he said, picking her up.

Ami was getting fiercer. The rain coming in from the sea was almost horizontal. The wind was picking up and swung around again.

"It's got to be at least a **category three** cyclone," Harry said.

"That means the wind speed's between 178 kilometres and 209 kilometres an hour, Harley," his mother added, explaining more about wind speeds in cyclones.

"I thought they measured cyclones by the amount of damage they did," Harley said, stroking Scruffy's nose. "I didn't realize it was wind speed."

"There's a scale," Harry said. "The **Saffir-Simpson Scale**. It starts with the wind speeds of tropical depressions. They have wind speeds of up to 62 kilometres per hour. It goes right through to a category five cyclone or hurricane. These storms have wind speeds of more than 250 kilometres per hour.

## Tuesday, 2.00 a.m.

Suddenly, Harry caught sight of movement in the double glass doors. With each gust, the doors bowed inwards then bounced back to their set position. He was aware that the bolts holding them were quite small and that the wind was getting too strong for the catches. They wouldn't last much longer. If the doors caved in, there would be shattered glass everywhere. Then the wind and rain would rip around inside the house like trapped wild animals.

With swirling winds in the house, everything would be smashed to bits. Loose objects would literally fly about the rooms, crashing against anything solid. He couldn't imagine the devastation. He didn't want to imagine the serious injuries flying glass could cause and

he didn't want to panic Jackie and Harley by
confiding in them.

He had to do something. Any delay now
could be disastrous. He had some planks of
wood in the shed. He'd be able to wedge the
doors with them – if he could get to the shed
and back with them!

There was no option but to open the back
door and make a dash for it. He knew the storm
was still hammering the other side of the house
but he wasn't sure how fast the winds were
swirling on the lee side. He had to take a risk.

He told Jackie his plan and got her and Harley
to push hard against the double doors to reduce
the amount of movement meantime. He didn't
spell out the consequences. Then he leaned
on the back door and slowly turned the knob.
To his relief, the door didn't push back against

his weight. He yanked it open, slammed it shut behind him and ran as fast as he could through the furious winds to the shed, dodging some of the small branches that whipped and rattled across the roof, dropped, and then flew into black oblivion.

He frantically grabbed several lengths of wood and stumbled back to the house. He didn't even notice that he was drenched for a second time that night. He awkwardly grasped the handle of the back door but just as he got inside, a large branch hit the roof with a frightening boom. Startled, Scruffy yelped, scrambled through Harry's legs, and bounded straight out into the raging night.

"SCRUFFY!" yelled Harley, as Harry slammed the back door. "SCRUFFY!" He started towards the back door.

"No, Harley!" Harry said. "Scruffy will go straight to her kennel. I need you here to help your mum and me. If we don't get these doors jammed we'll all be in serious trouble. We'll find Scruffy as soon as the wind dies down."

Harley was devastated, but something in his dad's voice warned him not to argue now.

"Scruffy will be OK," Jackie reassured him, not feeling nearly as confident as her voice implied.

"Keep holding the doors while I wedge the planks under the handles," Harry said. "Then, hold the wood while I nail it in place."

### Tuesday, 2.30 a.m.

After the doors were secure, they went into the kitchen. Through the window, Harley could see angry flashes of lightning. There was no time delay between the jagged flashes and the deafening roar of the thunder. He thought the storm must be right overhead. He couldn't get Scruffy out of his mind. Where was she? Was she hurt? What if she drowned? He felt a lump in his throat. He felt his eyes welling with tears.

"The wind's changed direction again!" his dad shouted. "It's blowing straight into the carport."

That was the last thing Harley needed to hear. He jumped up and headed for the back door just as a new river of water came from the direction of his bedroom.

"No!" Harry said, catching Harley by the shoulders. "You can't go out there. It's far too dangerous. We're all worried about Scruffy, but there's nothing we can do until the cyclone moves away and the wind dies out. Now get one of the mops and help your mum and me keep the water under control."

## Tuesday, 2.45 a.m.

Harley frantically mopped the floors in his bedroom and the bathroom. Even as he squeezed the mop out over the shower drain-hole, the water on the floor just got deeper. There was too much water in the house!

"I can't keep up with it!" he yelled to his dad above the uproar.

Harry grabbed a wet mat, rolled it up, and shoved it up against the base of the door. That helped a bit. He did the same for the other doors. Jackie rolled up towels and stuffed them on the windowsills.

A crash louder than any they had heard before startled them. Harley stood, heart in mouth, rooted to the spot. Was it Scruffy's kennel?

"That'll be one of the raintrees," Harry said, relieved that it hadn't hit the roof as it fell.

"At least it missed the house! The ground's **waterlogged** and the wind's just too strong. More will fall before this storm's over."

Harley wondered which one would go next. He loved those trees. He kept mopping, not sure it was doing any good but it kept his mind off things he didn't want to think about.

Soon he became aware of his dad standing still and listening. He stopped mopping and listened, too.

"The wind's eased," Harry said.

"It's getting warmer, too," said Jackie. "Probably because all the windows are shut!"

"There may be another reason," said Harry, looking up, "I think the rain's easing up, too."

"Is it over?" asked Harley. "Can I go out and get Scruffy now?"

"Not yet," answered Harry.

## *Tuesday, 3.00 a.m.*

Harry, Jackie, and Harley stood still, listening.
Harry was right, there was certainly a change in
the sound of the wind. There was less noise on
the roof, not much less, but enough to let them
know that the sea was still roaring angrily over
the reef and thumping the beach.

The rain had eased.

Harry headed for the double doors, nodding
to Jackie and Harley to follow. They wiped the
wet glass with their hands and peered into
the blackness. The rain suddenly stopped
completely.

"It has gone!" shouted Harley.

Jackie sighed and smiled at him.

"Stars!" shouted Harley, pointing. He was
right. Through the wet glass they could see a
scattering of shimmering stars.

Harry pressed his face to the glass. There was no movement in the doors. They were secure, at least for the moment.

"Can I get a torch and go and get Scruffy now?" Harley asked.

Harry didn't respond.

"Harry," said Jackie, "what's the problem?"

"Not sure, but I think it's the **eye** of the cyclone. That means we're at the halfway point. It's not over yet," he explained.

Harley looked at him, not understanding.

Harry tried to explain. "Think about how water swirls around the bathtub plughole. A swirling, spiralling mass of water's called a **vortex**. The outside water's swirling around quickly. The water right in the middle of the little whirlpool's hardly moving at all. That's where the eye is. The wind in a cyclone does the same thing. It has an eye and an **eyewall**. The eyewall surrounds the eye. It's got the highest surface winds in the cyclone. It could all start all over again very shortly. No looking for Scruffy yet. Sorry, Harley."

"I'll make some tea before we have to start mopping again," said Jackie, paddling to the kitchen. "We still have gas!"

"Good idea," agreed Harry. "What do you reckon, Harley?"

Before Harley could answer, Jackie called that the water coming through the tap was dirty. This meant the mountain steam had broken its banks. Soon the pipes would be carrying scraps of debris from the forest floor and the stream bed – leaves, bits of plants, and gravel!

Jackie made hot tea using water stored in the refrigerator. They sipped in silence. Talking was pointless. What more was there to say?

They were all tired, too. It had been a long night and there was more to come. They could hear the wind picking up and they knew what that meant. A scud of rain sideswiped the house. Then another, and another. Heavier and heavier and then the constant thumping and banging started again. The eye had passed. Ami was back with them!

The lights suddenly dimmed and Harry switched them all off, except one. The batteries were getting low and soon the whole system would automatically shut down.

Harley went back to the window and looked out, hoping to see Scruffy. He went to the back door and listened in case she was scratching to come in. No Scruffy. Nothing but Ami.

A savage gust of wind rattled the door. The wind had shifted direction again. It had moved around to the back of the house. Within minutes, it was howling and the rain seemed even heavier than before.

Harley was just about to go back to his mopping, when the house was shaken by a loud, metallic scrunching sound.

"That'll be the veranda from the house next door!" Harry shouted. He was glad it hadn't moved when he went out to the shed. Flying iron was more dangerous than falling trees!

Then the lights went out.

It was pitch black. In the dark, the noise seemed much louder. Harley stood still. He needed his eyes to get accustomed to the darkness.

"Where's the torch, Harley?" Jackie yelled above the roar.

"On the kitchen bench!" Harley yelled back.

"I'll get it!" yelled Harry. "You two stay exactly where you are."

He padded across the wet tiles to the bench, using his outstretched hands to guide him past furniture. He tapped along the bench top until he found the torch. Fumbling, he got it around the right way and switched it on. He shone it on Jackie and Harley.

"Come and sit with me at the table," Harry called. "Then I'll turn the torch off. I'll just use it to check the house now and again and for any emergencies."

It was a long, dreary wait, but was there nothing else they could do. Harley jumped at every loud, unexpected sound and thought about Scruffy. Every ten minutes or so, Harry checked the rooms. If nothing else happened to the house, they could wait it out.

## Tuesday, 5.00 a.m.

Dawn broke at five o'clock. The worst of the storm had passed. The rain had eased and the wind was beginning to drop. Jackie stretched her legs and went to the double doors.

"The houses around us are still standing," she said, relieved.

Harley looked out, too. The small valley was completely covered in water, banked right up to the road. Everywhere, coconut trees lay on the ground like fiddlesticks. As it got lighter, he could make out several very large uprooted trees on the hills.

Harry went to the bathroom. "There's no water," he called. "The pipes must be clogged, broken, or they've burst."

No radio. No phone. No power. And now no water. But plenty outside!

"Can I go outside and look for Scruffy now?" Harley pleaded.

"I'll go out and check first," his dad replied. "I want to make sure there's no broken glass or sharp bits of iron roof hidden in the flood waters. I also need to make sure there aren't loose things on the roof than could fall and hurt you. Wait a bit longer till the rain stops."

Harry went outside. It was still raining, but not pouring. They hadn't had any serious damage. The house and shed had survived. The solar panels looked undamaged. Soon he could start the generator and put some power back in the batteries and the house. They shouldn't leave the fridge off for too long. There was no knowing how long it would be before the road to town was cleared and they could get supplies. That's if the town had survived T. C. Ami.

He suspected it probably had, as it was about 20 kilometres away. Where they lived had taken the brunt of the storm. But time would tell.

There was no sign of Scruffy's kennel. It had obviously blown away. He gave a few sharp whistles. He waited. But Scruffy didn't come running. He feared the worst. He felt guilty because he had let her out. How would he tell Harley? He went back inside. He didn't smile.

Harley was looking out through the double doors, his shoulders were slumped. It was as if he already knew what his dad was going to say.

"Put your raincoat on, son," Harry said. "We'll go and look for Scruffy."

## Chapter 5

# *After the Cyclone*

*Early on Tuesday, January 14, 2003, Tropical Cyclone Ami headed south. It caused damage to Tonga and the Cook Islands. It finally weakened to an ordinary storm as it moved over the cooler waters of the South Pacific Ocean.*

"Her kennel's gone," Harry said as Harley headed out the door. Harley's heart dropped and his stomach churned. He thought he was going to vomit. He said nothing.

Then he found his voice and screamed, "SCRUFFY!" He screamed her name again and again and  kept on screaming as he frantically sloshed though the soggy ground and jumped over dead hibiscus bushes. But she didn't come bounding from anywhere.

"It's all your fault!" he screamed at his dad. "You shouldn't have let her out! You should have let me go out and look for her before! She's dead and it's all your fault!"

It was then that he saw the kennel. It was on the driveway, under the smashed roof of the neighbour's veranda. He ran to it and started to rip at the broken veranda tin, not caring that his hands were cut and bleeding.

"SCRUFFY!" he yelled again.

But as Harry got there to help him, Harley knew that if Scruffy was inside, she wasn't alive.

There was no sound. No whimpers. No barks. No growls. No nothing.

Harley could barely watch as his father lifted up the last piece of tin, and with a mighty grunt heaved the kennel over so that the doorway was visible.

"She's not here," Harry said, with a huge sigh of relief. At least she wasn't injured or dead in her kennel. But he knew that she might still be injured – or dead – somewhere else in the battered landscape.

"SCRUFFY! SCRUFFY!" Harley yelled again as he shot up and started running and yelling again. He didn't know where he was going. He just had to find Scruffy.

"Think straight, Harley," he heard his dad call after him. "Where would Scruffy go if she wasn't in her kennel?"

"Of course," thought Harley. "The big raintree with the hole in it."

He changed direction and headed back toward the house. But as he rounded the corner of the house, he stopped dead. The tree was on its side. It was the one that had fallen in the night! Now its mangled branches spread out across the lawn in a twisted, broken mess. Its base was sticking up in the air like a giant circular wall of dirt and webbing. The roots towered over him. Where was the hole?

Harley frantically scrambled under and through the wet leaves and over slippery branches calling Scruffy's name. He was breathing heavily, so heavily he wouldn't have heard a whimper.

"Scruffy!" he called desperately, as he searched for the hole that Scruffy would have run into.

He struggled through the drenched branches and dripping leaves and then he found the opening wedged hard against the ground. If Scruffy had been hiding inside then she would have been trapped – or crushed.

"Scruffy!" he called. "Scruffy!" Then he listened. But all he could hear was the still-angry waves crashing on the shore.

Then he heard it – a sad little whimper.

"She's here!" he yelled to his dad. "Dad, Scruffy's here!" His voice quavered as he scraped some loose soil away and rubbed his fingers across a little black muddy nose.

Harry arrived and they both started scraping desperately at the wet soil, pulling it away from the small opening as quickly as they could. Scruffy began pawing at the ground on the other side.

"She can move," Harley said, smiling.

But soon Harry realized that their digging efforts were futile.

"I'll go back to the shed and get a shovel," he said. "You stay with Scruffy and keep her calm. We don't want her hurting herself any more trying to get out."

It didn't take Harry long to get a shovel and he carefully removed enough soft, wet soil so that Harley could help Scruffy out. He clung to her. She was covered in mud but seemed unhurt.

"She needs a bath," joked Harry. "And now so do you, but we haven't got any water."

"More like she needs a good meal," said Jackie, who'd just arrived.

They went back to the house together. Harry surveyed the damage again.

"We're safe," he said. "Our job now is to clean up. First, the house, then the grounds. It'll take days but we're all alive."

"I think we should start with fixing Scruffy's kennel," said Harley. "That's the most important thing we have to do!"

# How much have you learned?

**1** What is the name of the scale used for measuring wind force?

**2** How are cyclones, hurricanes, and typhoons named?

**3** What direction from the Equator do northern hemisphere hurricanes move?

**4** What is the calm area in the middle of a cyclone called?

**5** How fast are the winds in a category 5 cyclone?

**6** What temperature must sea waters be at for a cyclone to occur?

# Literacy Skills and Knowledge

## Discuss

Once you have finished reading T. C. A*mi*, discuss with a classmate the events leading up to Tropical Cyclone Ami. What did the characters in the story do to track the approaching cyclone?

## Write

Write a time line of the events leading up to Tropical Cyclone Ami hitting Fiji. Using the book to help you, write down how the characters tracked the cyclone, from when it was a storm, to its hitting Fiji. Use the dates listed in the book to help you with the chronological ordering. Summarize each event. Include specific information only. Use the time line on page 65 to help order the events of the story.

| |
|---|
| Sunday, January 12 |
| • Harry hears news of a storm over the ocean |
| |
| |
| Monday, January 13 |
| |
| |
| |
| Tuesday, January, 14 |
| |
| |
| |

## Present

Once you have completed your time line present it to your classmates. Answer any questions your classmates may have about your time line.

# Science Skills and Knowledge

## Plan

Anemometers measure the speed of the wind. With a classmate, construct an anemometer and measure the speed of wind around your school.

You will need:

- Scissors
- A marker pen
- Stapler
- Push pin
- Watch with seconds
- 4 white paper cups
- 2 cardboard strips
- Pencil with eraser on the end
- Modelling clay

## Investigate

What to do:

1. Make an X with the cardboard strips. Staple the strips together.

2. Colour one of the white cups with the marker pen.

3. Staple the cups to the ends of the cardboard strips. Make sure the cups face the same direction.

4. Push the pin through the middle of the X on the cardboard and into the eraser on the pencil.

5. Blow the cups to make sure the card spins freely

6. Stick the modelling clay to a surface outside and stick the sharpened end of the pencil into it. Make sure your anemometer can stand up straight.

## Record

Using your watch, count the number of times the coloured cup spins around in one minute. Record your results. Continue recording the wind speed over the next week.

## Conclusion

Look at your results. Discuss with your classmate how the wind speeds varied over the week. What kinds of things happened in the weather that week that could have influenced the wind speed?

# Glossary

**Beaufort Scale**

a scale for describing wind speeds and effects

**category three**

a hurricane-force cyclone with winds between 178–209 kilometres per hour

**cumulus clouds**

flat-based, billowing clouds with a domed top, which can develop into storms

**cyclone**

a storm of winds that rotate around a centre of low atmospheric pressure

**depression**

areas of low atmospheric pressure associated with weather fronts

### Equator

an imaginary line drawn around the widest part of Earth

### eye

a circular area of light winds and fair weather found at the centre of a severe tropical cyclone

### eyewall

circular ring of deep convection which is the area of highest surface winds in a cyclone

### gusts

sudden blasts of wind

### humidity

the measure of the amount of moisture in the air

**hurricane**

in the North Atlantic Ocean, the name given to cyclones with winds of 119 kph or more

**northern hemisphere**

the half of Earth that is north of the Equator

**Saffir-Simpson Scale**

a scale for categorizing hurricane-force cyclones, according to the speed of their winds

**southern hemisphere**

the half of Earth that is south of the Equator.

**spiral bands**

narrow rainbands that seem to spiral out of the centre of the cyclone

**tropical storms**

cyclones with winds between 63–117 kilometres per hour

**vortex**

a swirling, spiralling mass of water or air

**waterlogged**

saturated with water – too wet to be manageable

# Quiz Clues

## Do you want some help?

**1** Go to page 28.

**2** Go to page 26.

**3** Go to page 14.

**4** Go to page 4 or 48.

**5** Go to page 6.

**6** Go to page 4.